Easy *Piano*

Love Songs
of the 80s and 90s

HAL LEONARD EUROPE
DISTRIBUTED BY MUSIC SALES

Exclusive Distributors:
Music Sales Limited
8/9 Frith Street, London W1D 3JB, England.
Music Sales Pty Limited
120 Rothschild Avenue, Rosebery, NSW 2018, Australia.

Order No. HLE90000781
ISBN 0-7119-8250-3
This book © Copyright 2000 by Hal Leonard Europe

Cover design by Chloë Alexander
Front cover photograph courtesy of SuperStock
Printed in the USA

Your Guarantee of Quality
As publishers, we strive to produce every book to the highest
commercial standards.
The book has been carefully designed to minimise awkward
page turns and to make playing from it a real pleasure.
Throughout, the printing and binding have been planned
to ensure a sturdy, attractive publication which should give
years of enjoyment.
If your copy fails to meet our high standards, please inform us
and we will gladly replace it.

Music Sales' complete catalogue describes thousands of titles and
is available in full colour sections by subject, direct from Music
Sales Limited. Please state your areas of interest and send a
cheque/postal order for £1.50 for postage to: Music Sales Limited,
Newmarket Road, Bury St. Edmunds, Suffolk IP33 3YB, England.

www.musicsales.com

ALL FOR LOVE

from Walt Disney Pictures' THE THREE MUSKETEERS

Words and Music by BRYAN ADAMS,
ROBERT JOHN "MUTT" LANGE and MICHAEL KAMEN

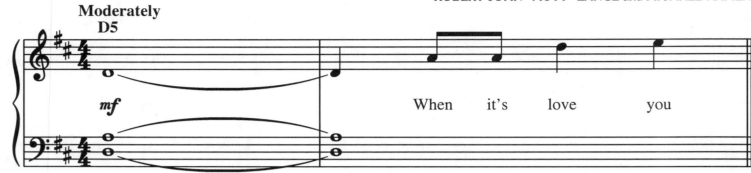

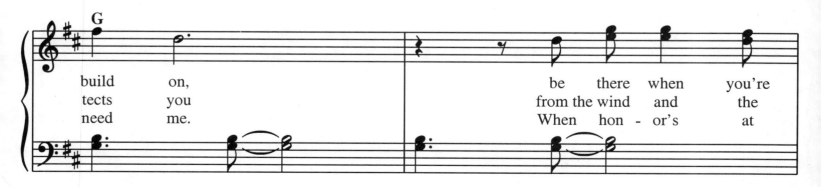

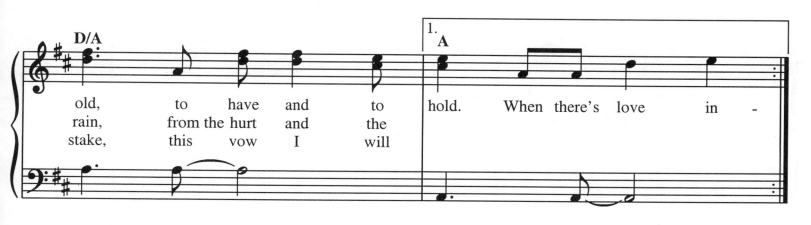

old, to have and to hold. When there's love in -
rain, from the hurt and and to the
stake, this vow I and the will

pain.
make:
Let's make it
that it's
all for one and all for

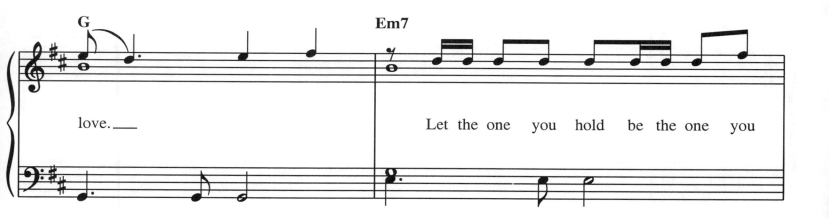

love. ___
Let the one you hold be the one you

want, the one you need, 'cause when it's all for one it's one for

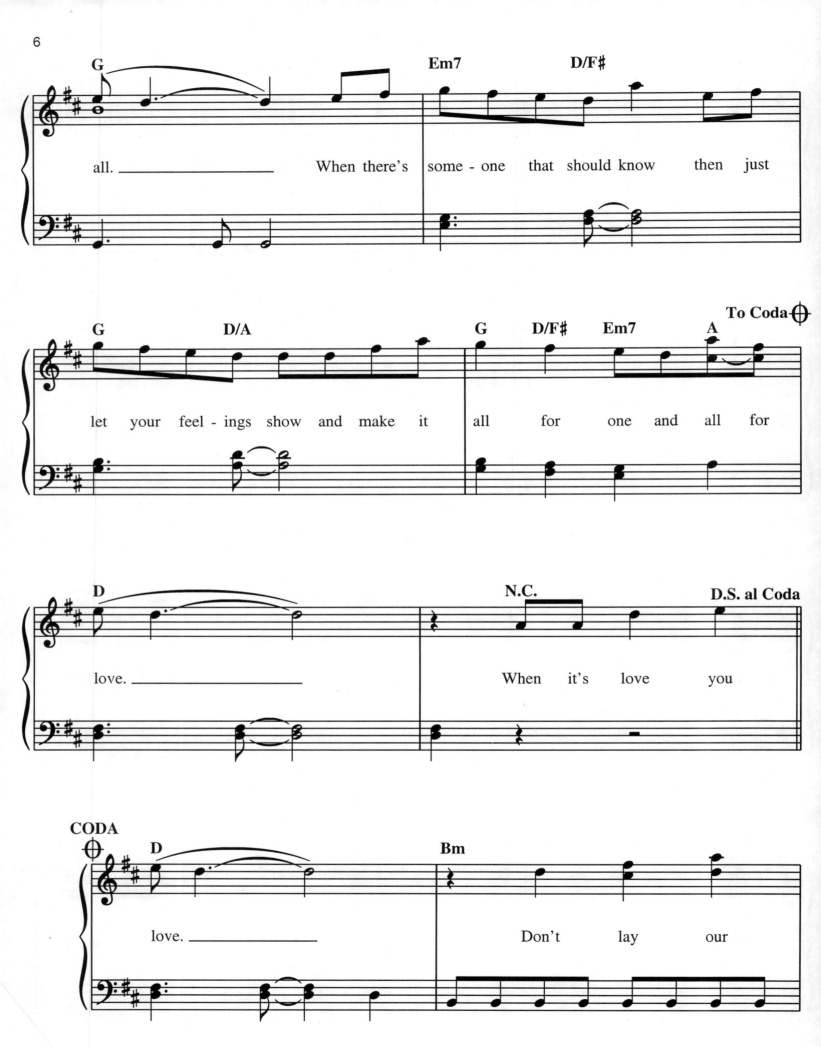

AMAZED

Words and Music by MARV GREEN,
CHRIS LINDSEY and AIMEE MAYO

Moderately slow Country Ballad

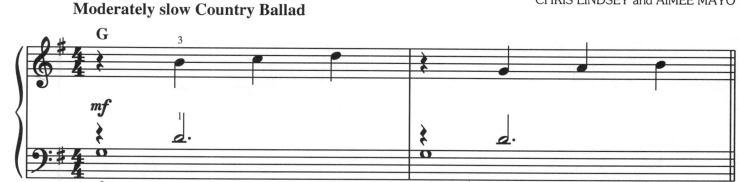

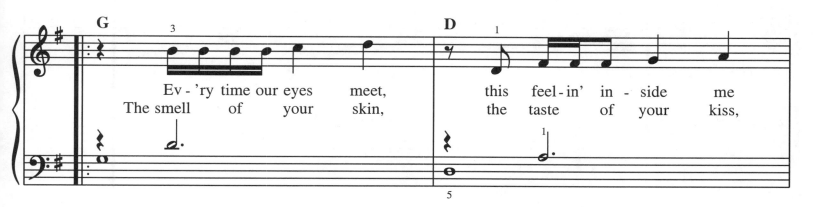

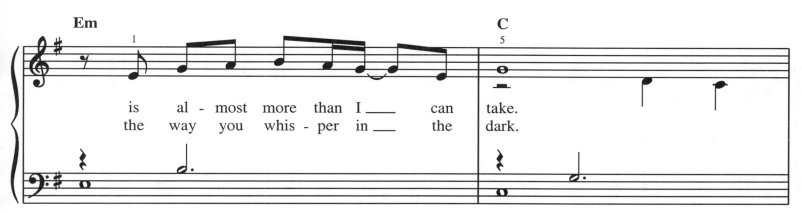

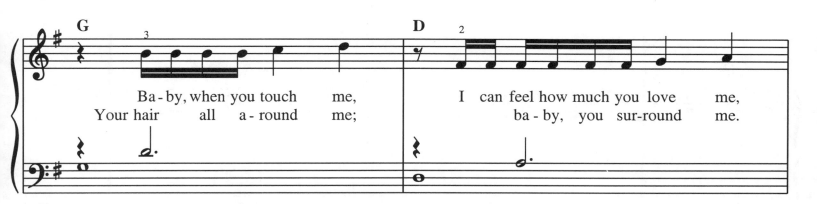

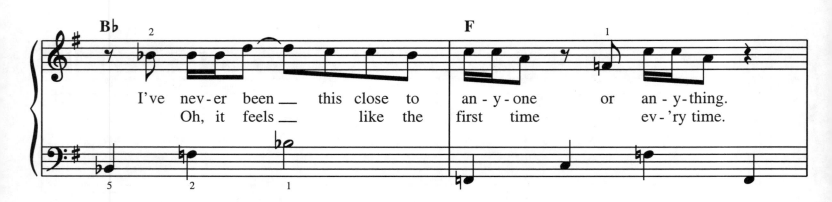

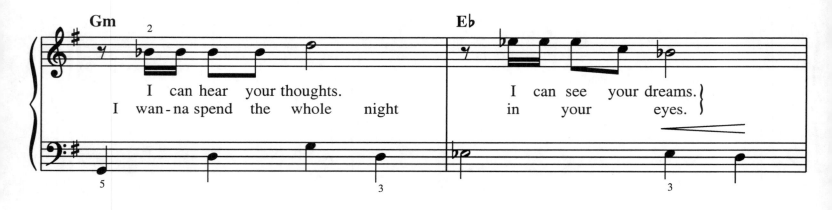

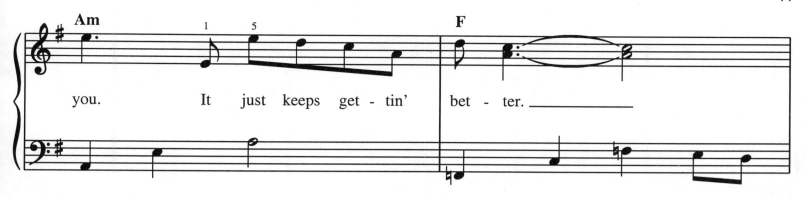

you. It just keeps get - tin' bet - ter. _____

I wan-na spend the rest of my life _____ with you by my side _____

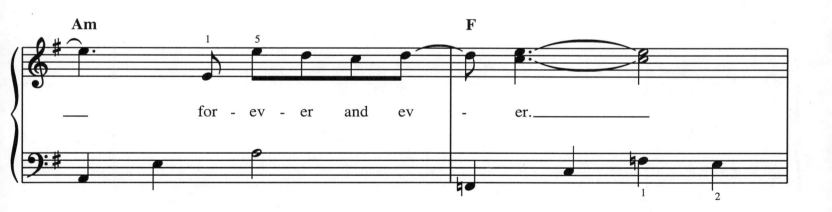

_____ for - ev - er and ev - er. _____

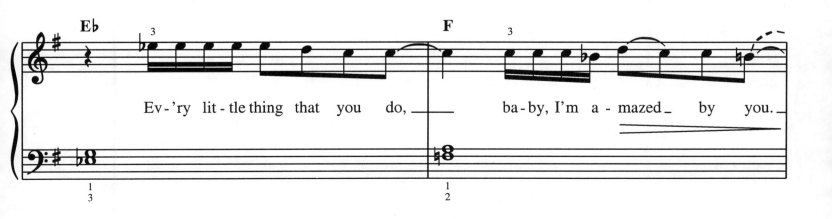

Ev-'ry lit-tle thing that you do, _____ ba-by, I'm a-mazed _____ by you.

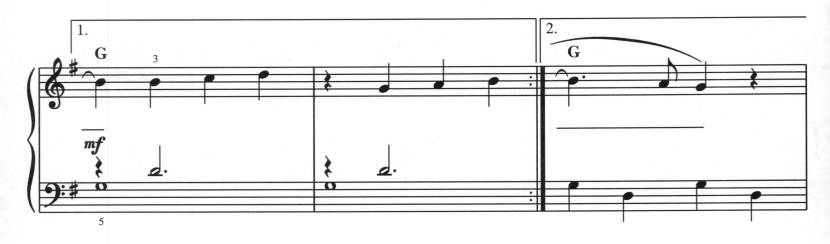

(Instrumental)

Ev-'ry lit-tle thing that you do.___ I'm so in love with you. It just keeps get-tin'

bet - ter. _____ I wan-na spend the rest of my life ___

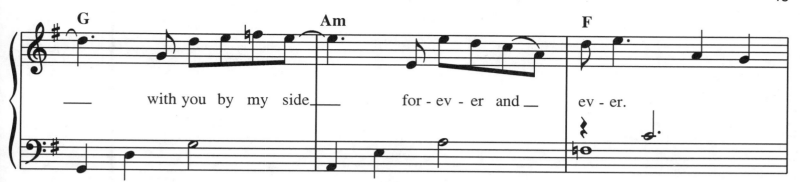

with you by my side ___ for - ev - er and ___ ev - er.

Ev - 'ry lit - tle thing that you do, ___ oh, ___

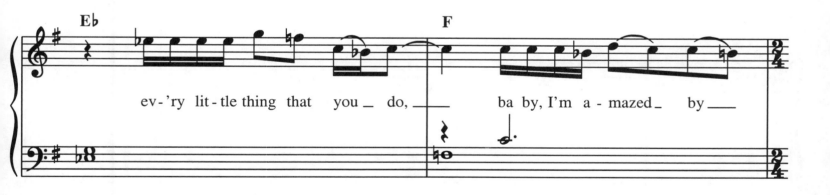

ev - 'ry lit - tle thing that you _ do, ___ ba by, I'm a - mazed _ by ___

you.

ALWAYS BE MY BABY

Words and Music by MARIAH CAREY,
JERMAINE DUPRI and MANUEL SEAL

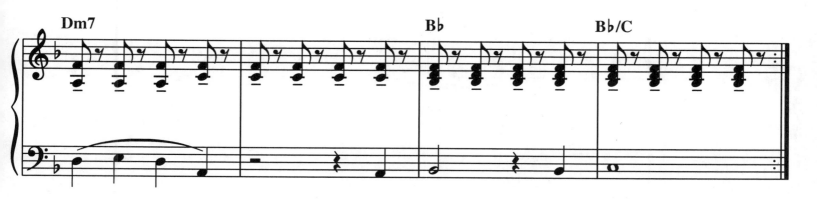

We were as one,___ babe, for a mo-ment in time.___
I ain't gon-na cry,___ no, and I won't beg you to stay.___

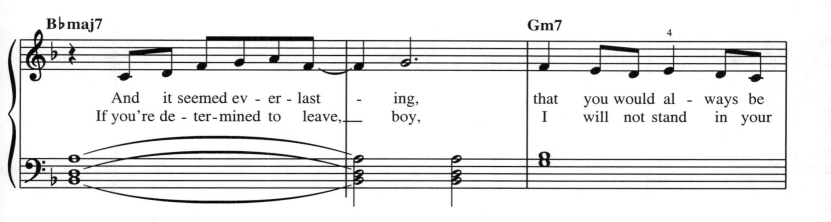

And it seemed ev - er - last - ing, that you would al - ways be
If you're de - ter-mined to leave,___ boy, I will not stand in your

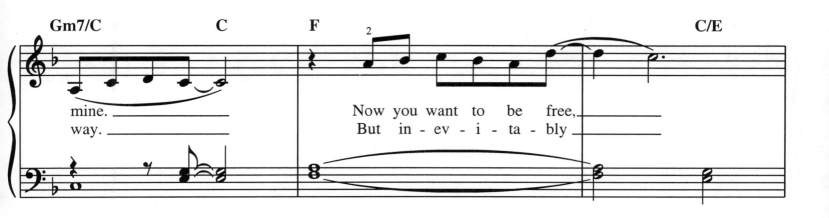

mine. _____ Now you want to be free,___
way. _____ But in - ev - i - ta - bly ___

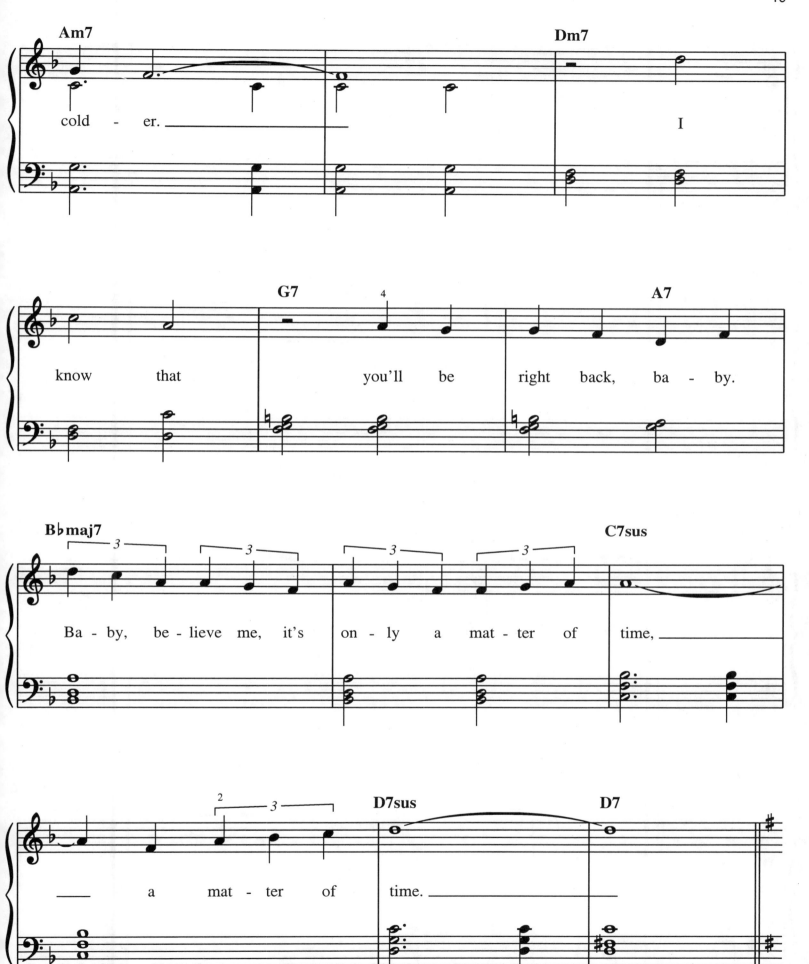

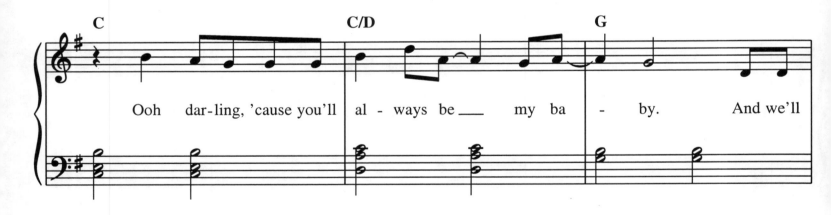

ANGEL

Words and Music by
SARAH McLACHLAN

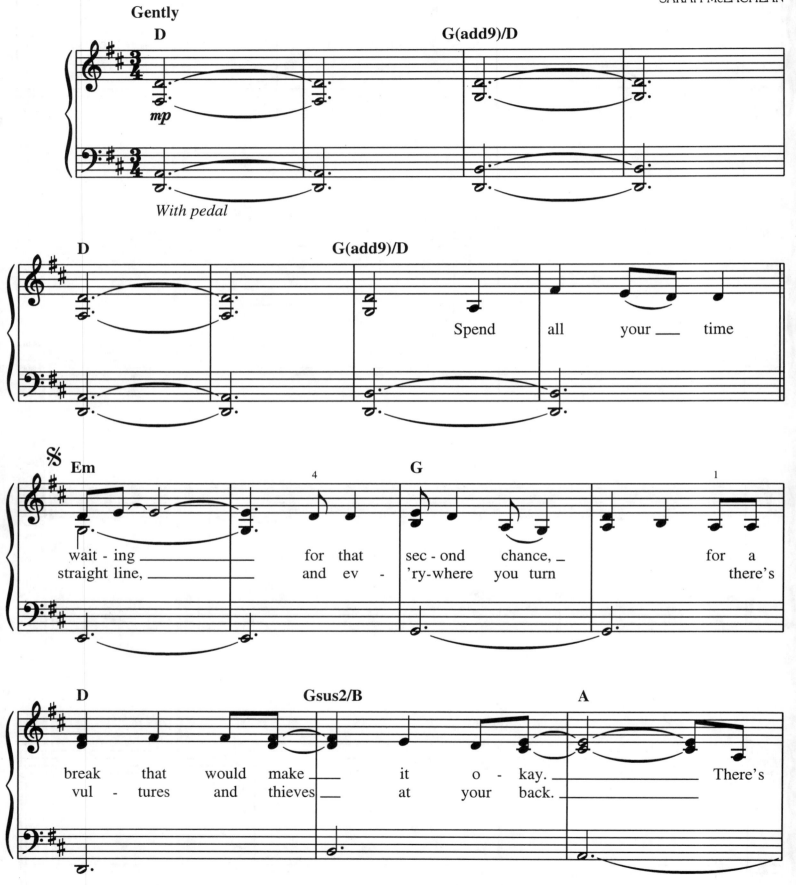

in the arms of the an -

gel. Fly a - way

from here, from this

dark, cold ho - tel room

28

CAN YOU FEEL THE LOVE TONIGHT

from Walt Disney Pictures' THE LION KING

Music by ELTON JOHN
Lyrics by TIM RICE

There's a calm _ sur - ren - der
There's a time _ for ev - 'ry - one,

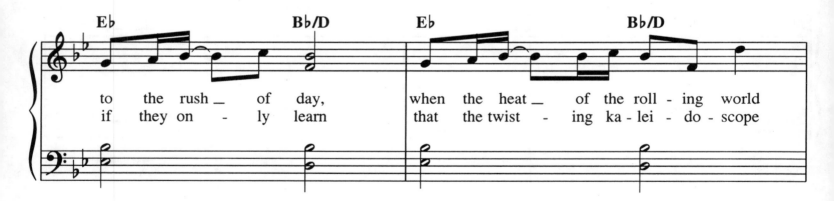

to   the rush _ of day,   when the heat _ of the roll - ing world
if   they on - ly learn   that the twist - ing ka - lei - do - scope

can   be turned _ a - way.   An en - chant - ed mo - ment,
moves us all ___ in turn.   There's a rhyme _ and rea - son

CHANGE THE WORLD

featured on the Motion Picture Soundtrack PHENOMENON

Words and Music by WAYNE KIRKPATRICK,
GORDON KENNEDY and TOMMY SIMS

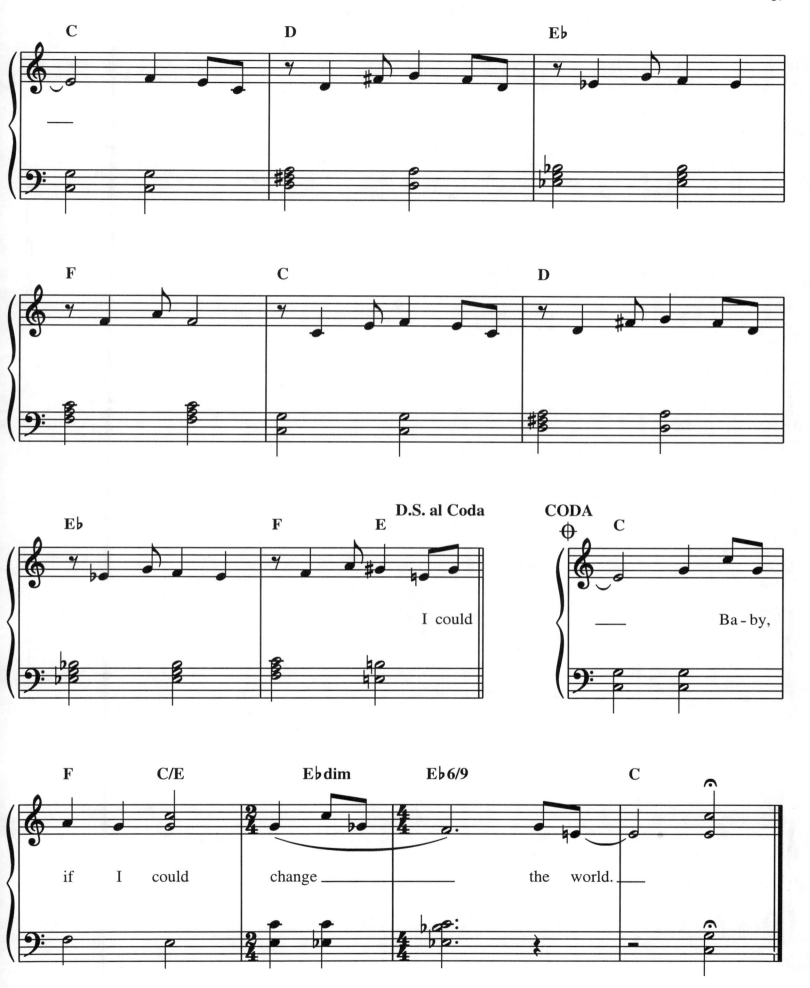

ETERNAL FLAME

Words and Music by BILLY STEINBERG,
TOM KELLY and SUSANNA HOFFS

FIELDS OF GOLD

Words and Music by
STING

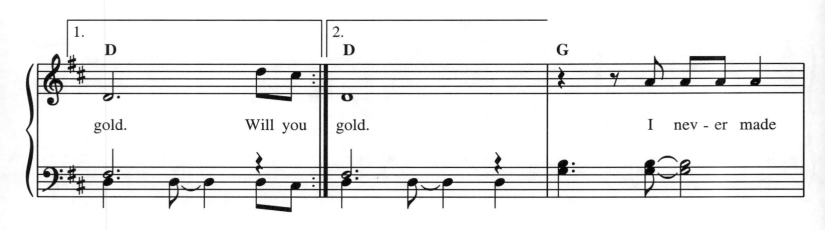

gold.   Will you   gold.   I nev-er made

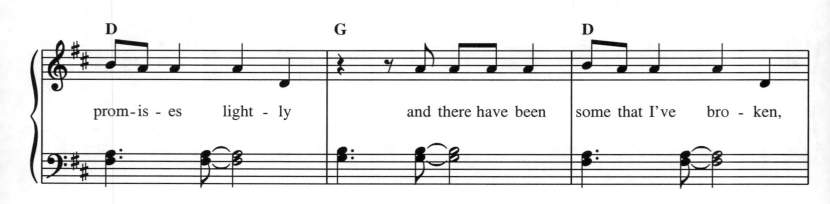

prom-is-es   light-ly   and there have been   some that I've   bro-ken,

but I swear __ in the   days still   left we'll   walk in fields __ of

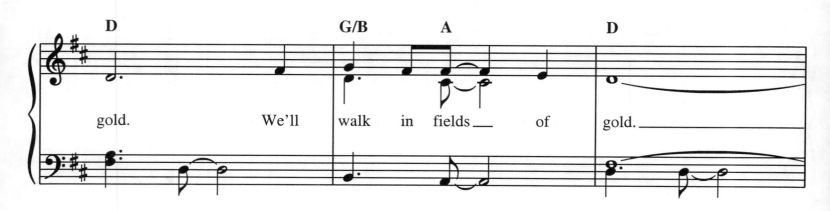

gold.   We'll   walk in fields __ of   gold. _____

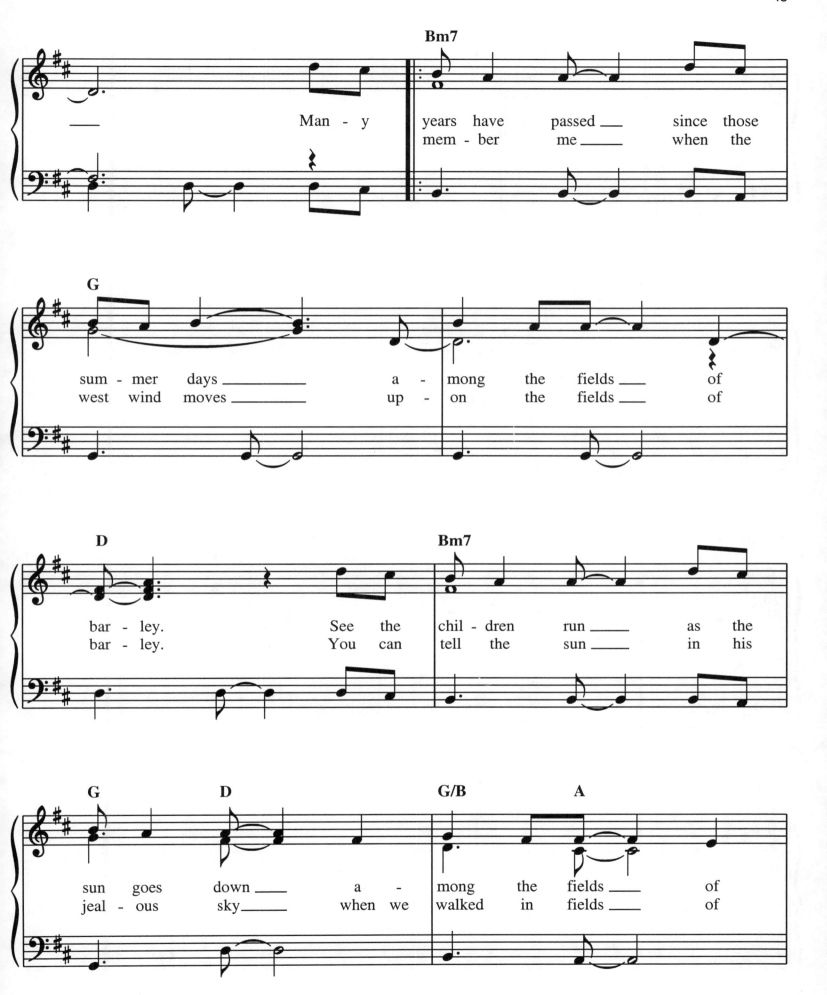

gold.   You'll re -   gold,   when we   walked in fields ___ of

gold,   when   we   walked   in   fields ___   of

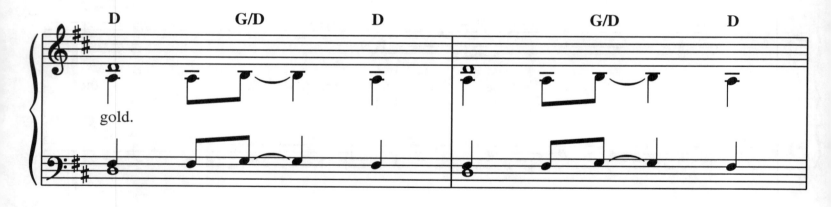

gold.

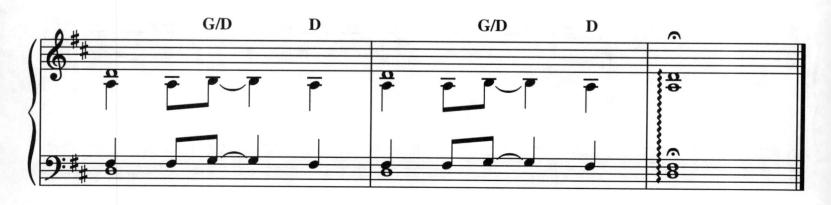

GROW OLD WITH ME

Words and Music by
JOHN LENNON

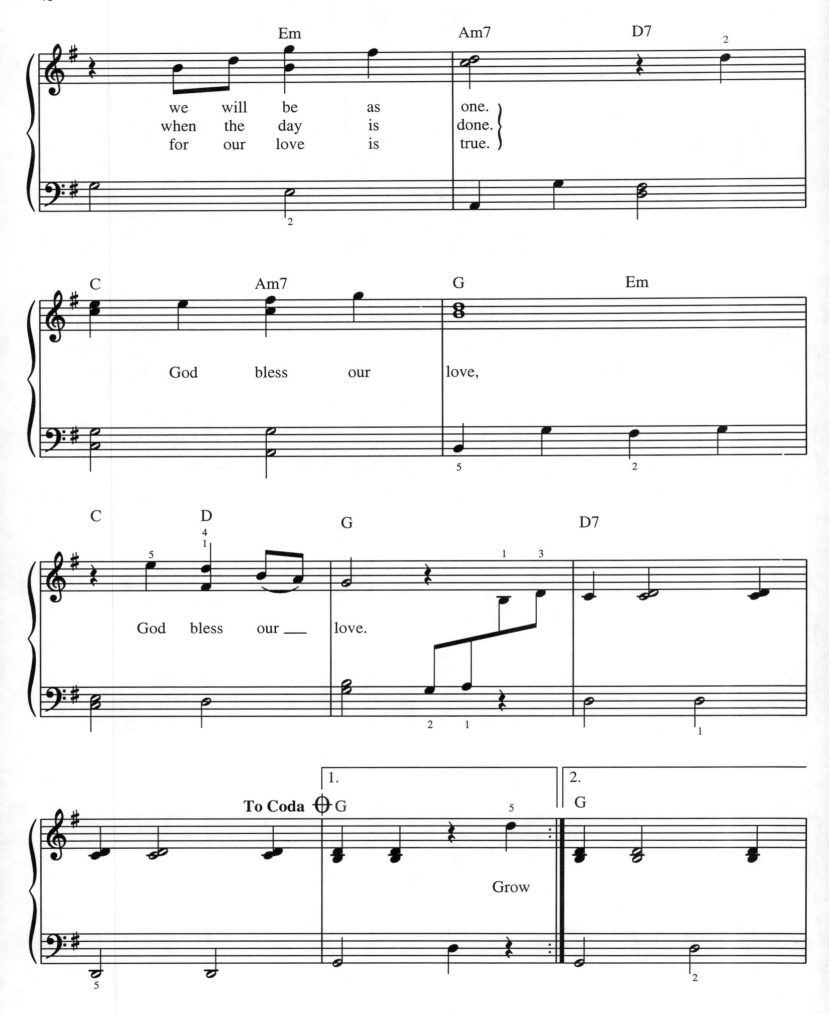

HAVE I TOLD YOU LATELY

Words and Music by
VAN MORRISON

Have I told you late-ly that I love you?___ Have I
told you there's no one else a-bove you?___ Fill my heart with glad-ness,
take a-way all my sad-ness, ease my trou-bles that's what you

I'LL MAKE LOVE TO YOU

Words and Music by
BABYFACE

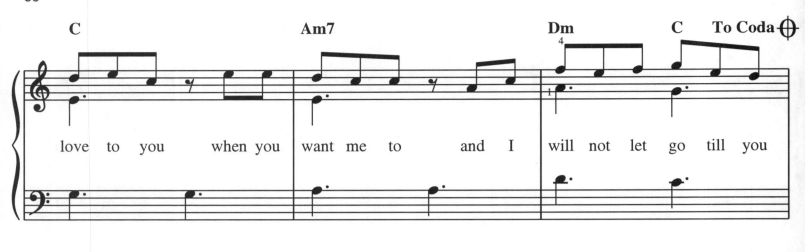

love to you when you want me to and I will not let go till you

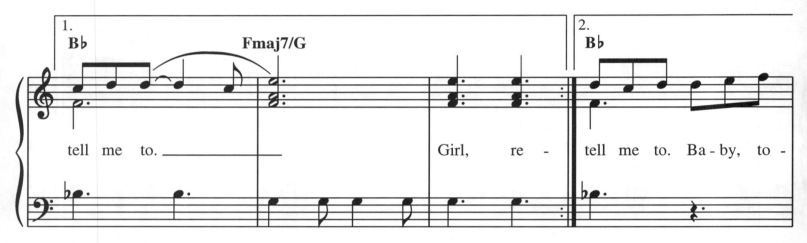

tell me to. _____ Girl, re - tell me to. Ba - by, to -

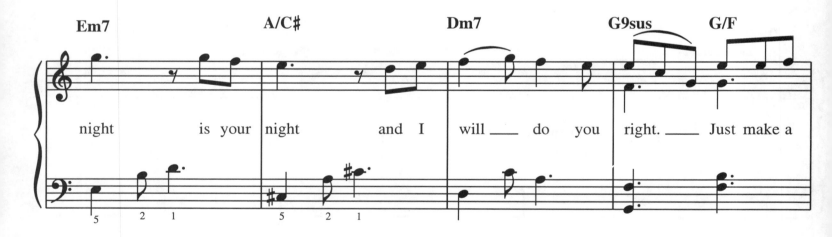

night is your night and I will ___ do you right. ___ Just make a

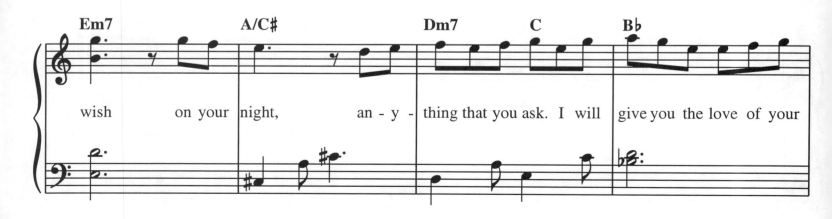

wish on your night, an - y - thing that you ask. I will give you the love of your

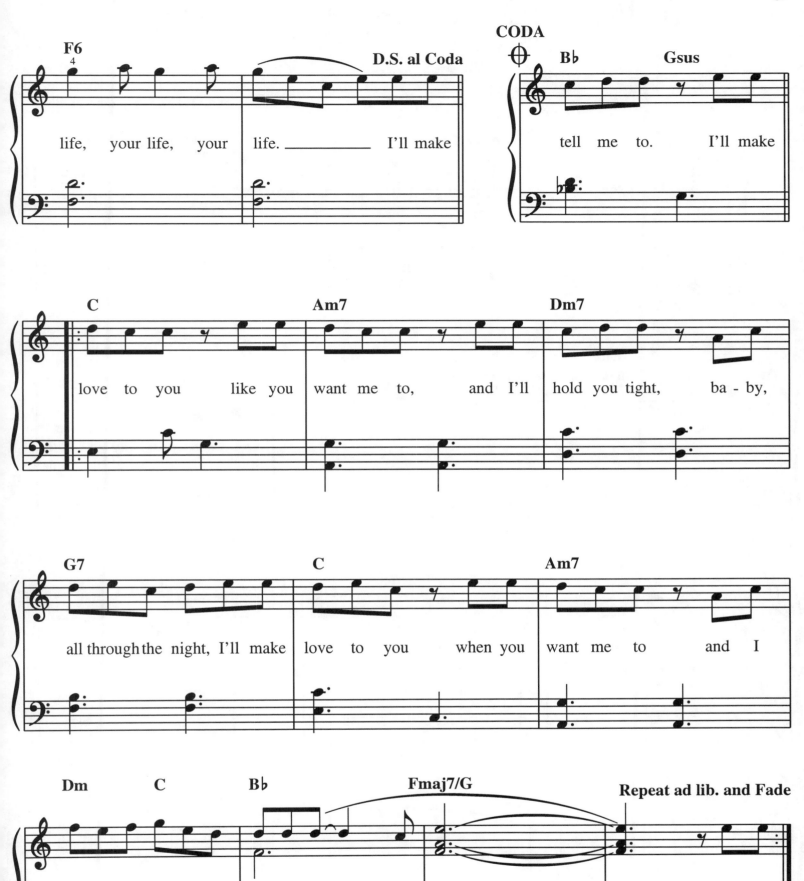

IF WE HOLD ON TOGETHER
from THE LAND BEFORE TIME

Words and Music by JAMES HORNER
and WILL JENNINGS

MCA music publishing

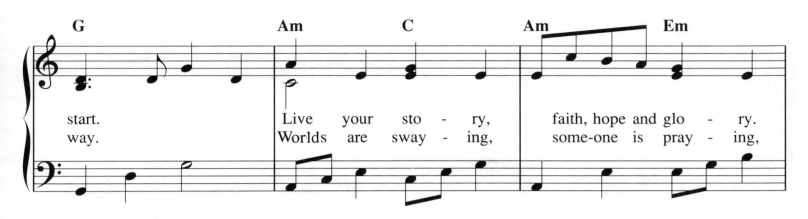

start.
way.

Live your sto - ry,
Worlds are sway - ing,

faith, hope and glo - ry.
some-one is pray - ing,

Hold to the truth in your heart.
please let us come home to stay.

If we hold on to -

geth - er,

I know our dreams will nev - er die.

Dreams see us through to for - ev - er where clouds roll _____

If we hold on to - geth - er

I know our dreams will nev - er die. Dreams see us through to for -

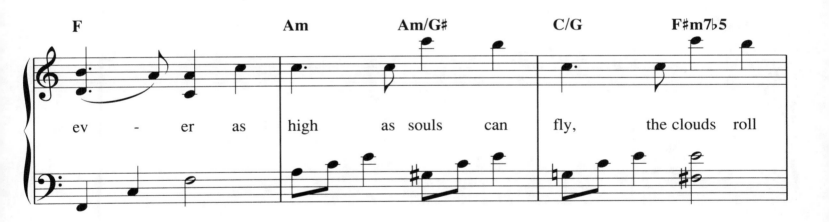

ev - er as high as souls can fly, the clouds roll

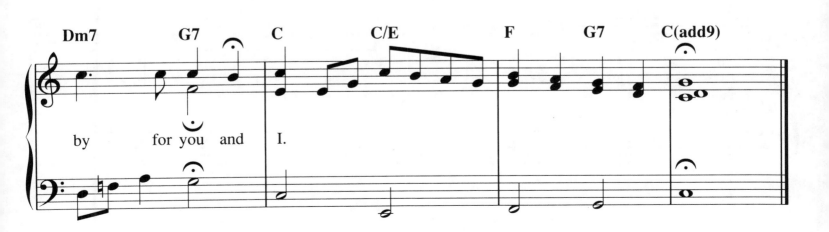

by for you and I.

SOMEWHERE OUT THERE

from AN AMERICAN TAIL

Words and Music by JAMES HORNER,
BARRY MANN and CYNTHIA WEIL

Moderately, with expression

MCA music publishing

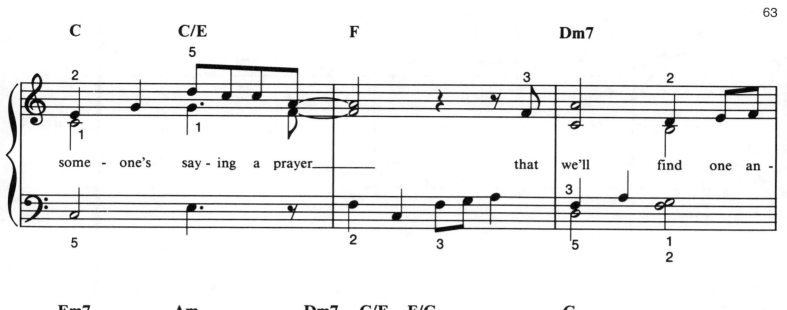

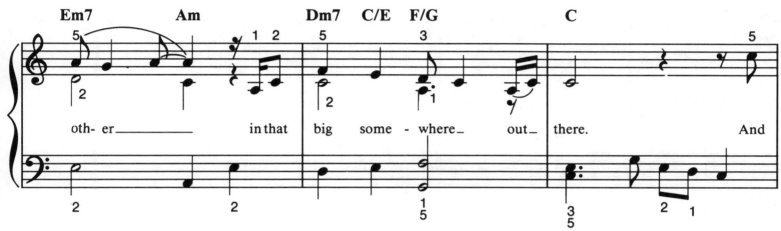

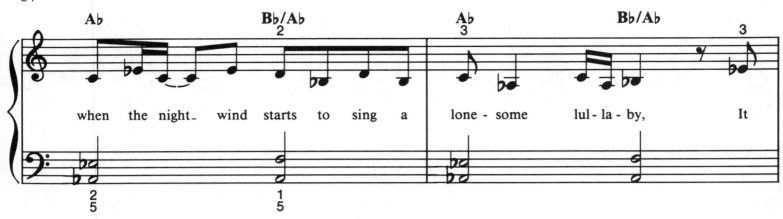

when the night wind starts to sing a lone - some lul - la - by, It

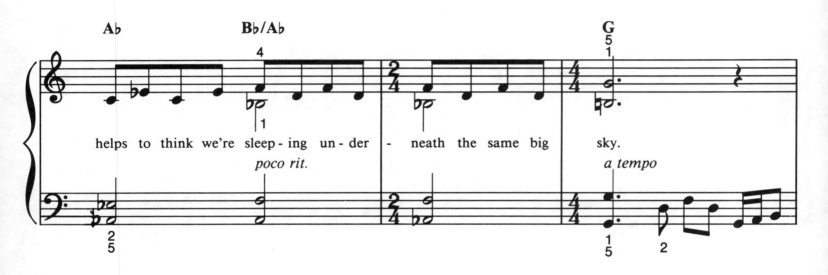

helps to think we're sleep - ing un - der - neath the same big sky.

poco rit.   *a tempo*

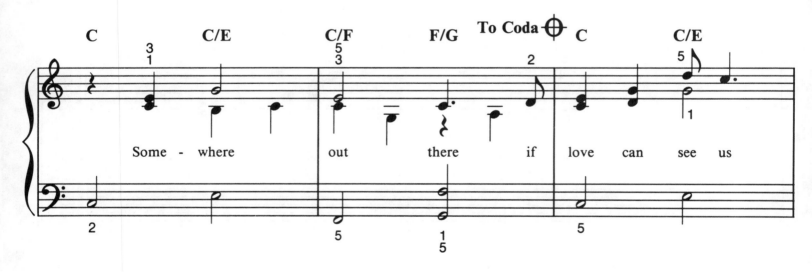

Some - where   out   there   if   love   can   see   us

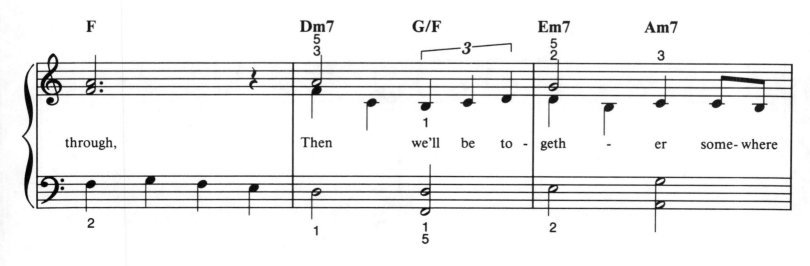

through,   Then   we'll   be   to - geth - er some- where

UNCHAINED MELODY

Lyric by HY ZARET
Music by ALEX NORTH

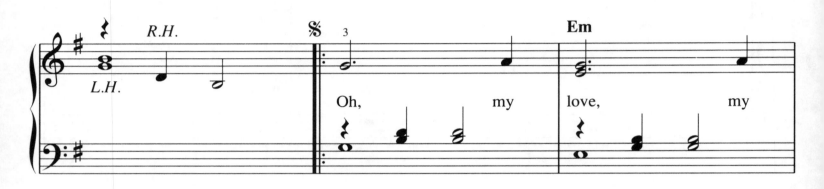

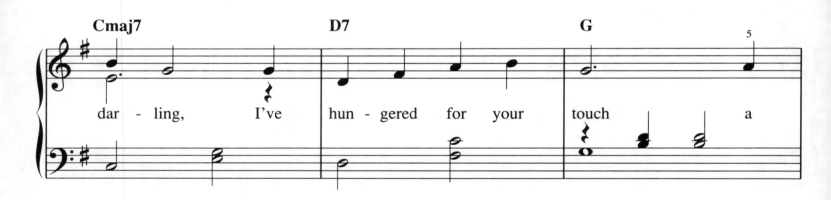

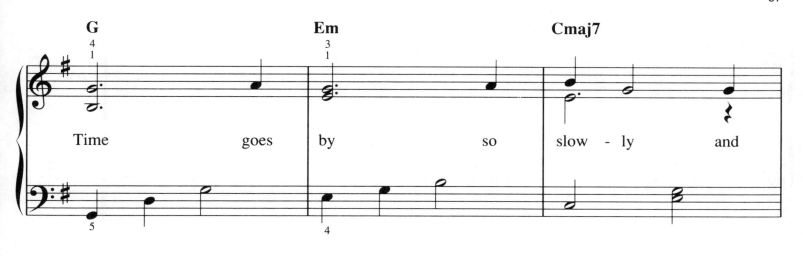

Time   goes   by   so   slow - ly   and

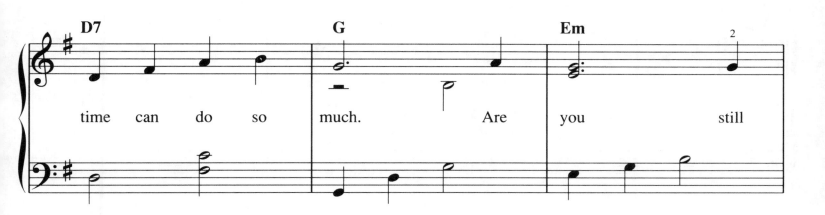

time   can   do   so   much.   Are   you   still

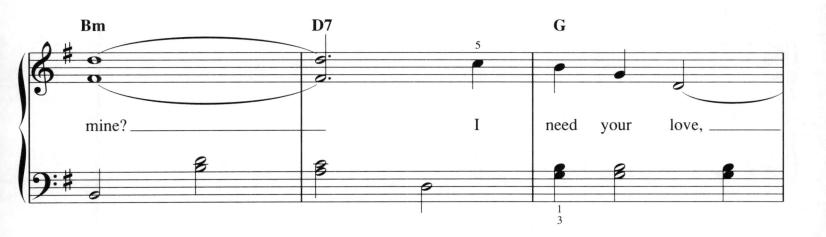

mine? _____   I   need   your   love, _____

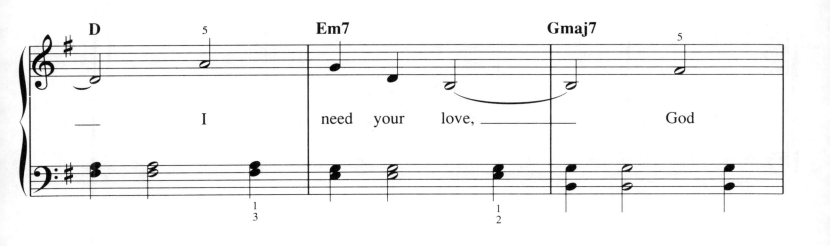

___   I   need   your   love, _____   God

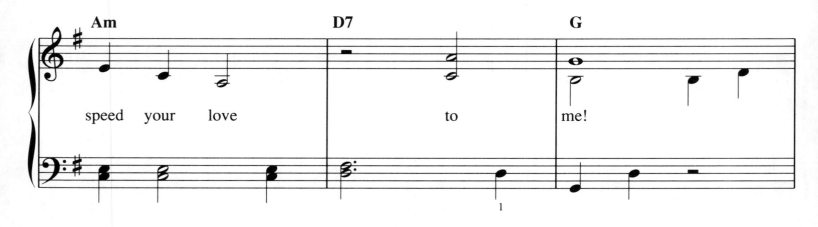

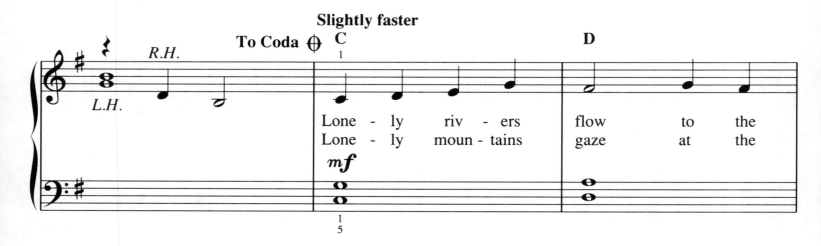

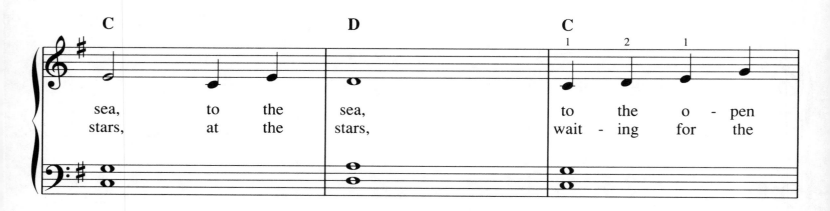

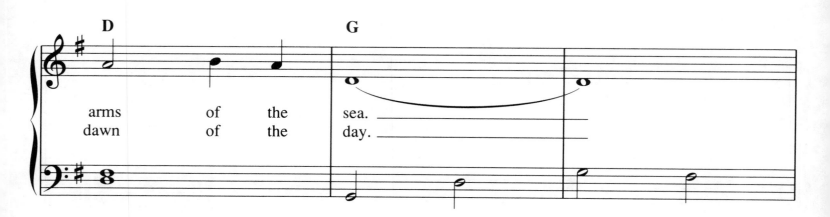

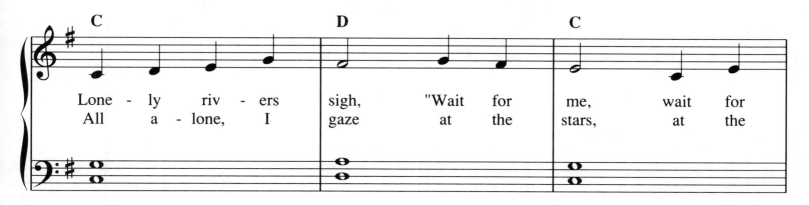

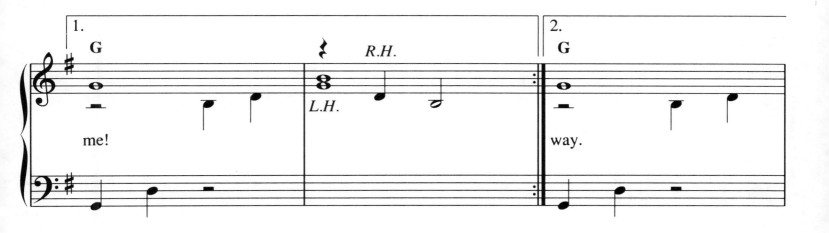

UP WHERE WE BELONG

from the Paramount Picture AN OFFICER AND A GENTLEMAN

Words by WILL JENNINGS
Music by BUFFY SAINTE-MARIE and JACK NITZSCHE

Slow and soulful

Who knows what to - mor - row brings; _ in a world, few hearts sur - vive? All I know is the way I feel; _ when it's real, I keep it a - live.

Some hang on to "used - to - be", _ live their lives look - ing be - hind. All we have is here and now; _ all our life, out there to find.

The

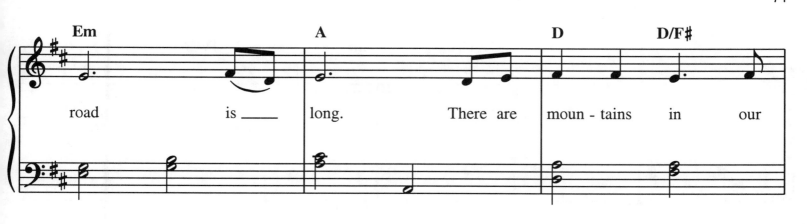

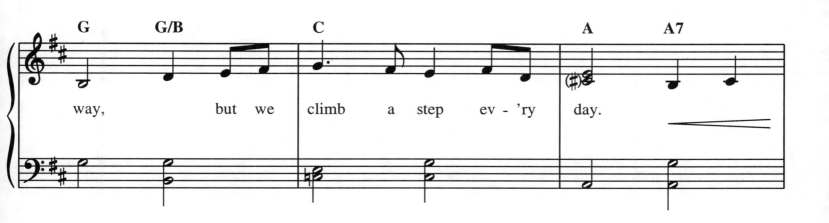

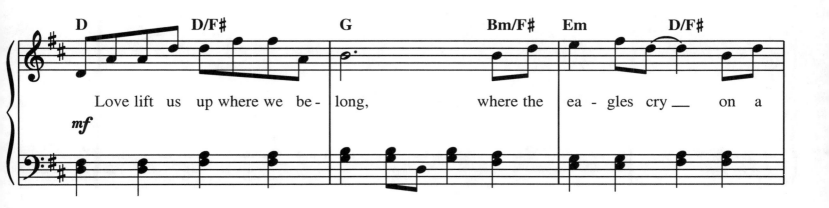

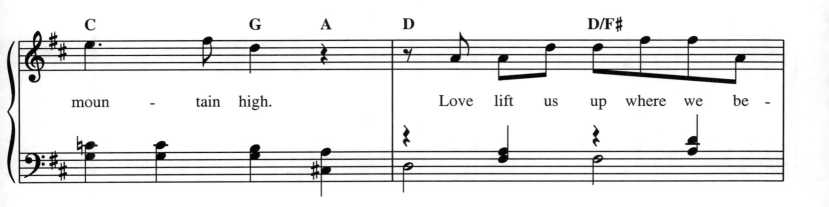

WHEN YOU SAY NOTHING AT ALL

Words and Music by DON SCHLITZ
and PAUL OVERSTREET

Moderately Slow

With pedal

It's a-maz - ing how you
All day long___ I can hear

can speak right___ to my heart___
peo - ple talk - ing out loud.___

With - out say - ing a word___ you can light up the dark.___
But when you___ hold me near___ you drown out the crowd.___

when you say noth-ing at all.

D.S. al Coda

The

CODA

when you say noth-ing at all.

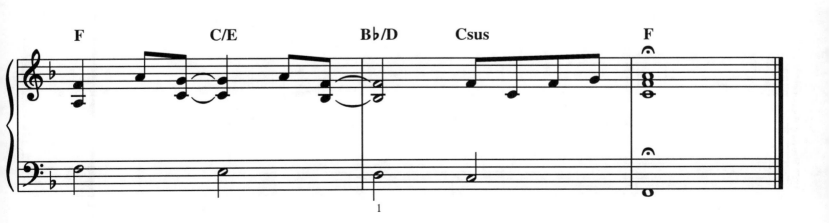

YOU'LL BE IN MY HEART

(Pop Version)
from Walt Disney Pictures' TARZAN™

Words and Music by
PHIL COLLINS

SAVE THE BEST FOR LAST

Words and Music by PHIL GALDSTON,
JON LIND and WENDY WALDMAN

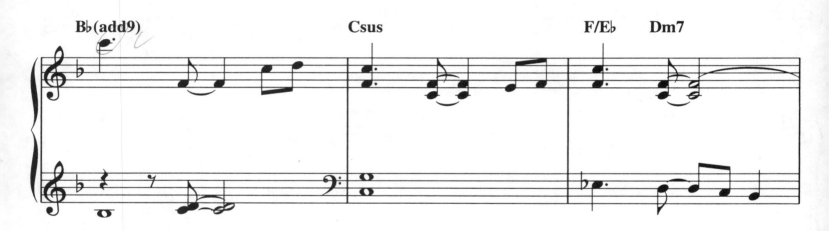

Some-times the | snow comes down_ in June. Some-times the
| nights you came_ to me when some sil - ly
| snow comes down_ in June. Some-times the

sun goes 'round the moon. I see the pas - sion in ___ your
girl had set ___ you free. You won-dered how you'd make ___ it
sun goes 'round ___ the moon. Just when I thought a chance ___ had

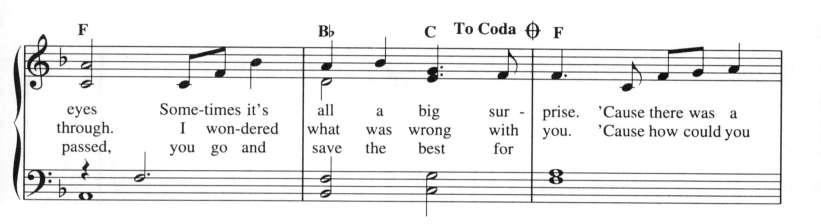

eyes Some-times it's all a big sur - prise. 'Cause there was a
through. I won-dered what was wrong with you. 'Cause how could you
passed, you go and save the best for

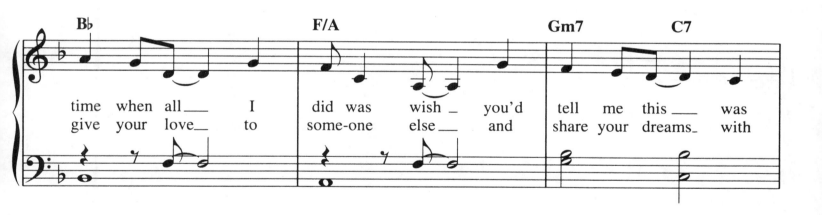

time when all ___ I did was wish ___ you'd tell me this ___ was
give your love ___ to some-one else ___ and share your dreams ___ with

love. It's not the way I hoped ___ or how I planned, ___ but
me? Some-times the ver - y thing ___ you're look - ing for _____ is the

some-how it's e - nough. And now we're stand-ing face __ to
one thing you can't see. But now we're stand-ing face __ to

face.
face. Is-n't this world a cra - zy place? Just when I

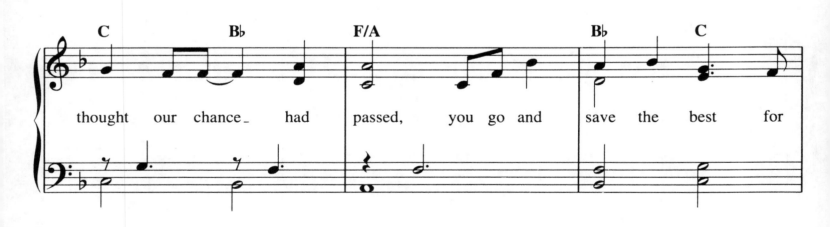

thought our chance __ had passed, you go and save the best for

last.

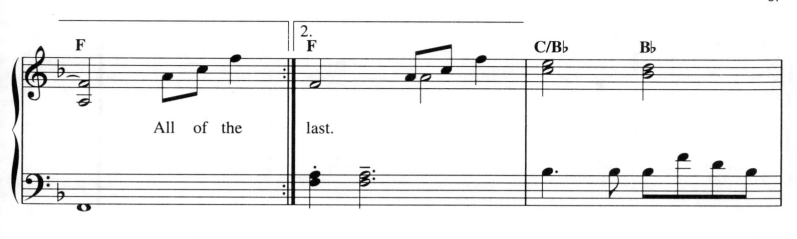

All of the last.

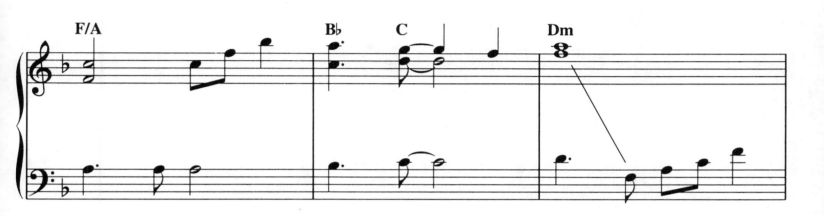

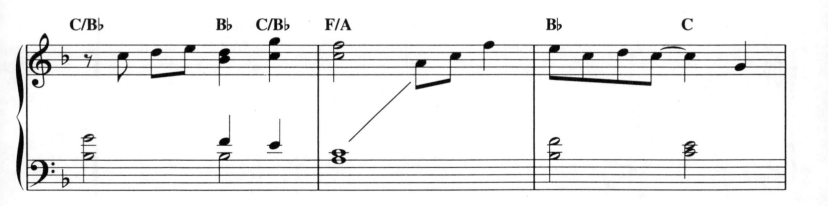

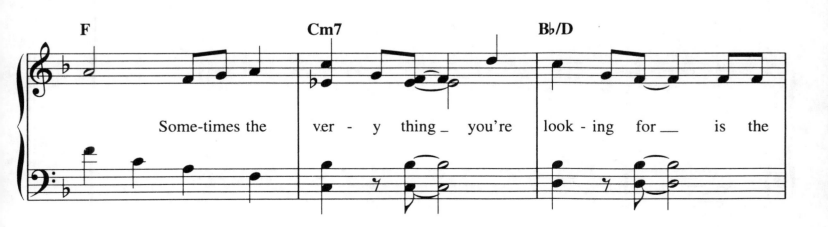

Some-times the ver - y thing _ you're look - ing for _ is the

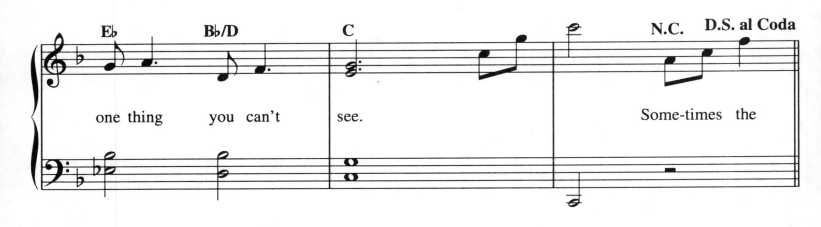